The Large Sandhurst Case, a set of brass instruments in a 13 inch (330 mm) mahogany case. Note the ivory sector, rectangular protractor and, in the base, the Marquoise scales. These instruments were supplied in 1880 by the Army and Navy Stores and were probably made by W. H. Harling.

DRAWING INSTRUMENTS
1850-1950

Michael Scott-Scott

Shire Publications Ltd

CONTENTS

Set in 9 point Times roman and printed in Great Britain by C. I. Thomas & Sons (Haverfordwest) Ltd, Press Buildings, Merlins Bridge, Haverfordwest, Dyfed.

British Library Cataloguing in Publication Data available.

ACKNOWLEDGEMENTS
The author wishes to thank Maya Hambly and Peter Stevens for their great encouragement and technical help; June Cronk for obtaining so many interesting items to illustrate; Michael Dunlop for his tubular compass; John Leaf for his dotting pen; Don Hayter for his skilful work in the restoration of certain items; and John Cozens LBIPP, for his untiring and most able processing of the photographs. The author is grateful to Sotheby's for kindly allowing him to reproduce their photograph of the Elliott Brothers military case of instruments.

COVER: *A large mahogany case of instruments dated 1889, containing two trays. One of its 6 inch (152 mm) ivory scales lies behind the rolling brass parallel rule and protractor; both were made in 1920. In the box are vulcanite set squares and French curves.*

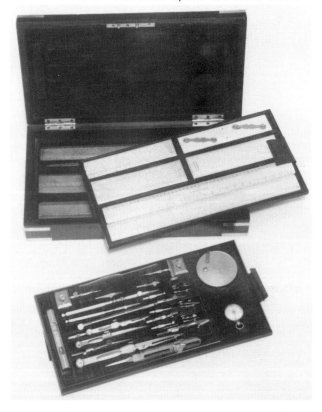

LEFT: *A fine and unusual set of instruments made by Elliott Brothers about 1885, sold at Sotheby's in 1985. The spirit level and tape as well as the ivory protractor with verticals suggest it was made for an army officer.*

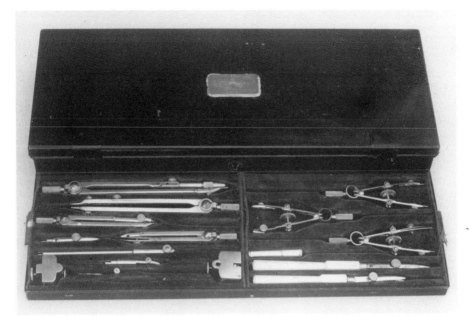

A set of instruments by W. H. Harling, dated 1936. The black japanned metal case was intended for use in the tropics, where mahogany might not survive. The two pens are later than the Second World War.

INTRODUCTION

Since early times man has made drawings and has employed devices of one kind or another, no matter how primitive, to assist him in creating sketches of objects he might wish to make. Even a piece of cord attached to a stake with a marker at the other end could be regarded as an instrument for drawing circles. The Romans had drawing instruments not so different in shape from those we use today. The great builders and carpenters of the middle ages required much more elaborate devices for developing the geometrical patterns which form the basis of the magnificent tracery seen in the windows of cathedrals. By the eighteenth century a few skilled craftsmen, making beautifully decorated and embellished items for wealthy patrons, had given England a high reputation in instrument making. Heath, Adams, Cary, Schmalcalder and Elliott, to name only a few, had set the standards.

In the nineteenth century there was a huge upsurge in demand for better, more accurate instruments. Engineers, architects and soldiers, faced with their rapidly developing technologies, stimulated the great increase in production. In Europe several famous makers appeared whose lighter instruments presented a challenge to the more traditional, heavy English design. Those produced by Haff and Riefler in Germany and by Kern in Switzerland were, and still are, among the finest available. In England W. F. Stanley took the lead in fending off European competition. After working in obscurity for a few years he launched his firm officially in 1853. One of his earlier apprentices, W. H. Harling, had already left him and set up in business on his own in 1851, founding a company which, for a hundred years, rivalled, but also collaborated with, Stanley's. The two firms produced most of the finest instruments

3

of the day. Not only did they make a wide range of catalogued items, they also developed sophisticated machinery with which to manufacture them. Many of their items were patented. When the patents expired some of the designs were widely copied and so the traditions were carried forward to the twentieth century. Well known firms, such as Halden of Manchester, A. G. Thornton (another of Stanley's apprentices) and Norton and Gregory, became leading suppliers of the highest class of instrument, joining the older companies Elliott Brothers, Cary and Archbutt.

By the 1920s and 1930s brass and silver had largely given way to electrum (an alloy of pure nickel and copper) in the construction of instruments. Most of the top-grade items were machine-made but hand-finished by dedicated craftsmen. Stanley claimed that this was why his firm was able to guarantee the head joints of its best compasses for a lifetime. In 1929 Harling ceased making compasses of the classical English design and went over to producing lighter, flat-limbed instruments which closely resemble modern ones.

By the end of the Second World War instruments of the classical type had become rather expensive, the volume of production had dropped and, perhaps because of marketing difficulties, the demand had fallen away. By 1960 W. F. Stanley had ceased trading in this field, though W. H. Harling, now Blundell Harling Limited, continued to make excellent drawing equipment. Today the PS range of Haff instruments, together with those of Riefler and Kern, come the closest to the best pre-war English instruments, in quality if not in shape. New materials such as heavy chrome (on brass), bright stainless steel for screws and tungsten carbide steel tips for pens are in vogue, but the instruments are again becoming very expensive. The slightly increased demand, particularly from the rapidly expanding graphics industry, is now met by companies such as Faber-Castell, Rotring and Staedtler.

When Victorian and Edwardian instruments appear on the market they are often very tarnished and so their high quality may be overlooked. A little time spent in restoring them, itself a fascinating pastime, reveals their true worth as objects which are beautiful to look at and delightful to handle and which will serve their new owners for generations.

Three pocket sets of spring bow compasses. The knurled handles of the set on the left, by Stanley, are particularly fine.

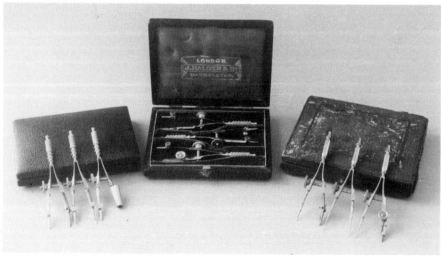

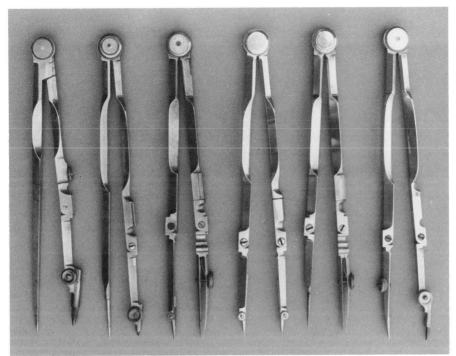

A selection of compasses by prestigious makers. The three on the left are in brass, the others in electrum. The compass on the extreme left dates from 1860, that on the far right from 1936. All have the celebrated sector head joint.

COMPASSES

Compasses are for drawing circles, in either pencil or ink; if they have only needle points, they become dividers. Although compasses look much the same the world over, there can be enormous variations in quality. A good compass must have a movement which is very smooth, to allow it to be set accurately to any radius, and which is neither too stiff to allow the limbs to be set accurately without jerks nor so loose that the setting, once achieved, may accidentally be altered in the course of normal, gentle handling. The principal joints must not wear easily nor develop lateral play. The instrument must be reasonably robust and not liable to corrode in harsh climates. Lastly, the compass must feel attractive and well balanced in the hand.

All these requirements were met by the high-quality instruments described here. It was the sector head joint that gave the smooth movement, a joint that was resistant to wear and play and yet easily adjusted with a special key. These joints were formed of two metals, the material of the compass (electrum, silver or brass) moving in contact with a steel bearing about a central steel pin. These sector heads gave the instruments their characteristic appearance and seemed to contribute to the balance.

All the instruments of the period had deep hollows cut in their arms. The purpose of these was to assist in the accurate setting of the compass. If the closed instrument was held between the thumb and forefinger over the hollow, slight pressure of the fingers would cause the compass arms to move open a small

5

ABOVE: *The sector head joint dismantled. Beeswax was the lubricant which gave the joint such a fine movement. Oil was never used.*

BELOW: *The deep hollows in the compass arms permitted the limbs to be opened very finely by pressure between the fingers. The dividers in the hand have the ordinary needle clamps, which were not ideal.*

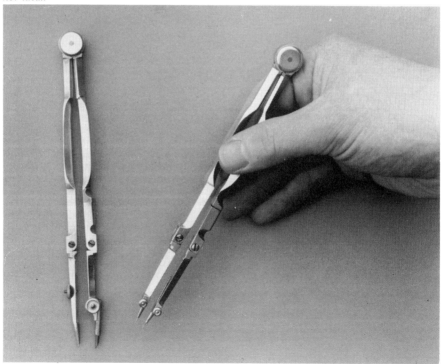

amount, setting them accurately to the desired radius.

It has always been important to be able to bring the pencil point, and more especially the point of the pen, down vertically on to the drawing surface. This was achieved by having knuckle joints in each of the compass arms. Lesser instruments had the knuckle joints in only one arm, leading to an awkwardness of setting and operation when extended a large amount.

It was in the mid nineteenth century that the sharp points of the instruments were perfected. Before then, solid, well tempered and beautifully shaped steel points had formed an integral part of the compass arm. Unfortunately an accidental fall could bend and ruin the points and render the whole instrument useless. The first solution was to have replaceable points, formed by ordinary needles, which were located in tiny clamps at the ends of the arms and secured in position by the tightening of small screws. Although this development found favour in many quarters, it was not ideal since there was a tendency for the needle to move unless very tightly gripped, and making the clamps was far from simple. It was the highly innovative and ingenious instrument maker W. F. Stanley who produced the ultimate solution. He developed and patented his so-called A and B needle points. The A points were spring-loaded and were recommended for tracing or inking-in finished drawings since they left no perceptible mark on the paper. (They are rarely to be found today.) The B points were ideal for general work and were always preferred in the highest class of instrument. Indeed, when the patents expired they were widely copied and eventually superseded all other designs. In effect they offer two points of support to the needle, which remains firmly held in position with little tightening of the screw.

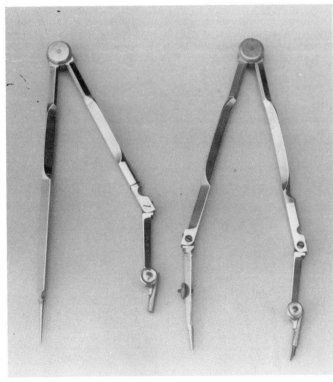

The compass on the left has a knuckle joint in only one arm and so is much inferior to the other which has these joints in each arm as well as the fine B needle points.

7

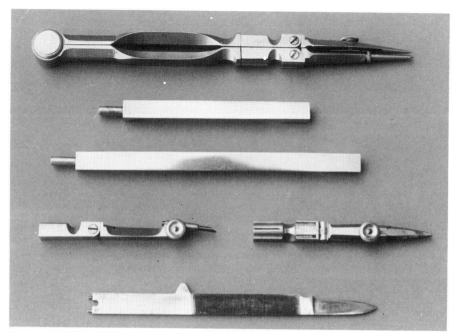

A top-grade half set by Stanley, 1879. The compass has both the special A and B needle points, which are interchangeable. Note also the two extension bars and the universal adjusting key.

Bow compasses were designed for drawing small circles or arcs, which is not easy with a larger instrument. They were simply miniature versions of the standard compass made either with a pencil or a pen arm, not interchangeable, and having a special turned or milled head to allow the compass to be finely rotated between the fingers. They varied in length between 3 inches (76 mm) and 3¾ inches (95 mm). All the earlier instruments had beautifully turned heads. Stanley introduced the milled head, which although less attractive in appearance was much more efficiently moved between the fingers. Turned heads had virtually given way to the milled type by about 1900.

The smallest circles were drawn with *spring bow compasses*, generally 2½ to 3 inches (64 to 76 mm) long. In these instruments the two arms were formed from a single piece of high-quality spring steel, held under tension by a screw; circles of a radius as small as a millimetre could be drawn with comparative ease. It

was standard practice to fit these compasses with slender milled handles and to offer them in sets of three — pencil, pen and divider. The points were commonly plain, though it was possible to obtain the standard and B-type needle fittings if required. Draughtsmen often preferred the plain point in all its simplicity since it was felt that the screw heads required to hold needles in place might obstruct the view when adjusting the instrument to the finest settings.

A rival to the spring bow compass was the *pump* or *drop bow compass*. Here the arm bearing the pencil or pen could drop down the pointed shaft, positioned accurately on the drawing surface, and the smallest of circles, perhaps of one millimetre radius, could be described by rotating the knurled head between thumb and third finger while holding the point in position on the drawing by pressure from the second finger of the same hand, a technique in common use today.

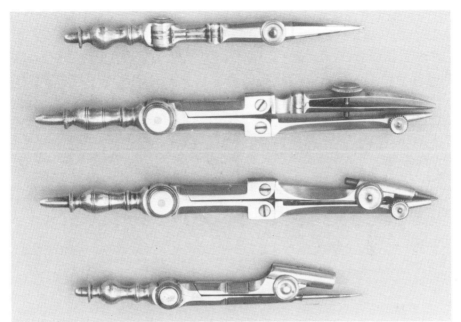

ABOVE: *Four bow compasses with attractively turned heads. The two outer ones were made in 1860; the two in the centre date from 1890.*

BELOW: *Some bow compasses with knurled heads, all about 1900.*

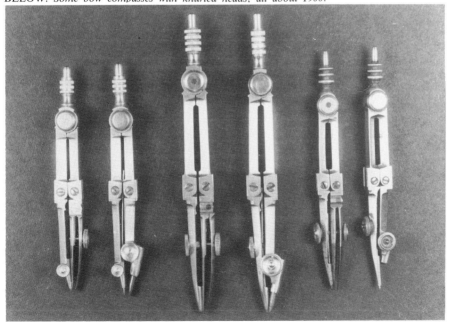

9

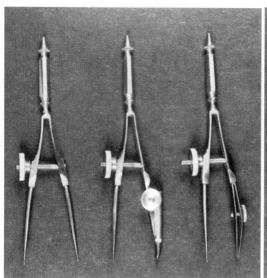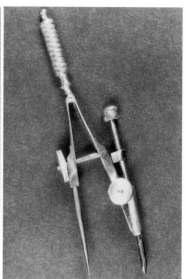

ABOVE LEFT: *Three spring bow compasses by Stanley, about 1860. The hexagonal handles had largely disappeared by 1880.*
ABOVE RIGHT: *A rare spring bow compass by Harling, about 1910. Note the special screw adjustment for the pencil lead, designed to take up wear on the point and to act as a back stop for the lead.*
BELOW: *Two small and very useful drop bow or pump compasses by Harling, about 1938.*

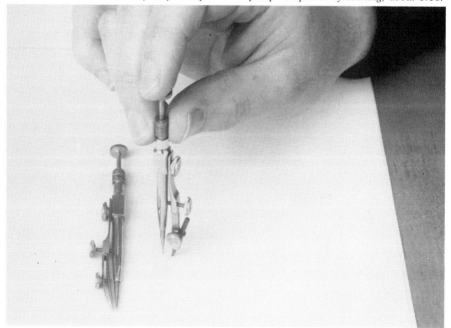

10

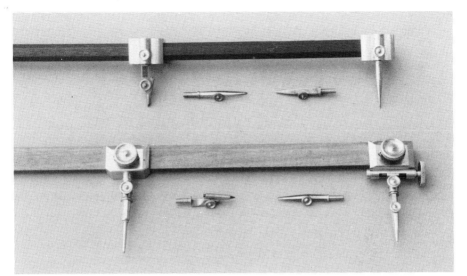

Two beam compasses. The sliding heads of the upper one, supplied by Norton and Gregory, are held tight to the shaped beam by internal springs. The heads of the lower compass, by Stanley, dating from 1875, have interchangeable A and B points and can utilise rules for the beam (or lath) if desired.

Circles of large radius had to be drawn with *beam compasses* or *trammels*, of which there were several designs on the market. A trammel consisted of a beam or lath, perhaps 3 feet (1 metre) or so in length, along which two sliding heads, each carrying a pen, pencil or point, could be positioned, in some cases with extreme precision by means of a vernier scale. All the best trammels had slow-motion, fine screw adjustments on one of the heads. The radius of the circle that such an instrument could draw depended on the length of the beam, which could be supplied to meet the individual requirements of the customer. The beams were made of mahogany, to which holly or boxwood scales were sometimes fitted. Finely divided scales were often of electrum. It was essential that the beam was

The Woolwich pattern beam compasses, about 1900. The beam was usually 36 inches long (914 mm). A vernier scale could set the radius to an accuracy of 0.01 inch (0.3 mm). The lower compass has a micrometer setting to one of the heads for even greater accuracy.

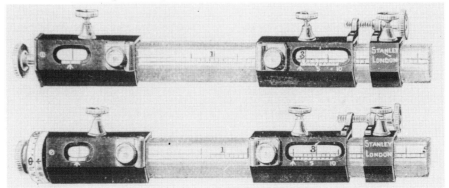

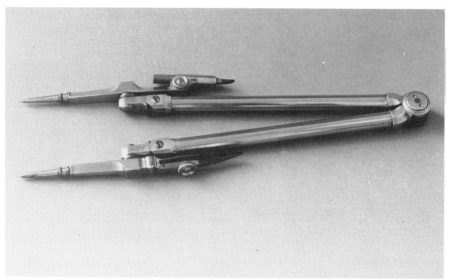

A fine tubular compass by Elliott Brothers, about 1880. Note the spring-loaded points.

rigid since any flexing would introduce gross inaccuracies in the drawing. Tubular and T-section beams were employed to overcome this problem.

Another type of compass is the *tubular compass*, an admirable and extraordinary instrument. It is said to have been invented by Marc Brunel at the end of the eighteenth century and it was still available after 1900. It was a device capable of drawing circles of from 0.1 inch up to about 14 inches (3 to 350 mm) in radius. As the name suggests, the outer arms

were tubes in which the inner arms could slide out or back like a trombone, albeit rather tightly. Each inner arm carried on one side a head consisting of a pencil and a point and on the other a pen and a point, so that by rotation any combination of pencil, pen or point could be set up. The draughtsman could adjust the compass accurately with the two points in position and then, by rotating one or other of the heads, bring either the pencil or the pen into use, should he wish to describe arcs or circles. These compasses

The arms of the tubular compass extended.

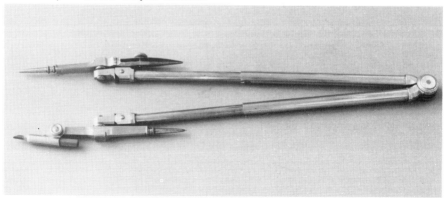

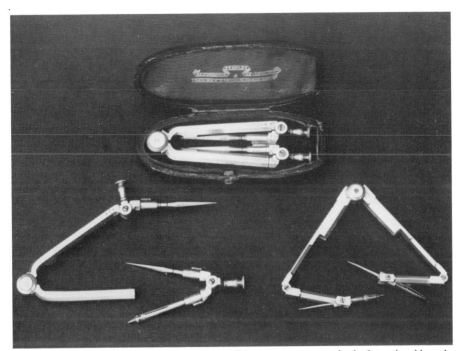

Two pocket or pillar compasses showing how small bow compasses can also be formed and how the points, pencil and pen can be accommodated in the arms. The device on the lower right is a fine Napier compass, an even more compact version of the pillar compass.

could be bought as separate items with their own cases and carried in the pocket. Not many appear to have survived in good condition.

The desire for portability was satisfied by the most elegant and magnificently constructed pocket or *pillar compasses*, small folding devices with inner arms which could be drawn out to form any combination of pen, pencil or point. Furthermore, either of the inner arms could, in isolation, form a bow compass with a pen or pencil arm; some even included a lengthening bar. Thus these compact devices represented virtually complete sets of instruments which could be carried unobtrusively in any jacket pocket. They embody all that was finest in late Victorian craftsmanship and today are occasionally seen in use as highly prized personal possessions.

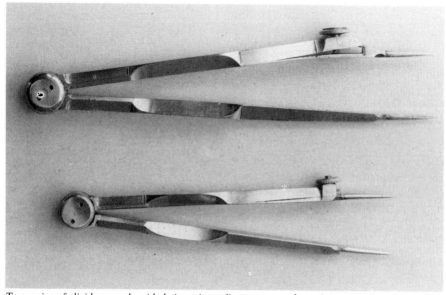

Two pairs of dividers, each with hair-spring adjustments on the points.

DIVIDERS AND COPYING AIDS

Dividers are widely used for measuring and stepping off lengths in a range of applications, a task they perform with greater accuracy than a compass because they have such fine points. Hair-screw adjustments on spring-leaf mounted points enabled some to be set to an accuracy of 0.01 inch (0.3 mm). Such dividers were very popular and were nearly always included in cases of instruments. Many have survived in good condition.

Triangular dividers or compasses were in existence by the middle of the nineteenth century. In essence they were simply an ordinary pair of dividers with the addition of another sector head joint, a sort of universal joint, to carry a third arm. Thus it was possible to use the device to fix three points simultaneously on a plan and to transfer them together to another drawing, thereby determining the lengths of lines and their orientations in one operation. Such instruments were considered to be extremely useful in copying mechanical drawings. Unfortu-nately they are very rarely found today, probably because they were not made in large quantities.

The most elaborate and expensive instruments in this field were the *proportional compasses*, which were dividers capable of several ingenious operations. They consisted basically of two slotted limbs that could move about each other around a sliding pivot whose position could be adjusted by a tightening screw. Each limb had steel points at either extremity, long and beautifully shaped at one end, short at the other. If the two limbs were opened about the pivot, the distance between the long points would be in a particular ratio to the opening of the short points, the value of this ratio being determined by the position of the sliding pivot. Almost any ratio up to 10:1 could be formed by setting a mark on the slider to a scale designated 'lines' or 'lineal ratios' (for the more common fractional ratios), marked on a face of one of the limbs.

The best proportional compasses were

14

'fully divided' that is, engraved with four scales on four separate faces of the limbs. The scales were denominated 'lines', 'circles', 'plans' and 'solids'. The scale of circles was for finding the lengths of the sides of inscribed polygons (generally up to twenty sides). The opening of the small points gave the length of the side of a polygon whose number of sides was set on the scale, while the opening of the large points defined the radius of the inscribing circle.

The scale of plans was designed to enable the areas of some regular plane figures to be decreased or increased by the ratio set on the slider, the large and small points respectively defining the sides of the large and small figures. A mathematically inclined user would quickly deduce that this process could yield the square root of the length set off by the large points.

The scale of solids allowed the volumes of regular figures to be stepped up or down in a given ratio by using the instrument in the same way as when it was set to the scale of plans.

Proportional compasses were often found in expensive magazine cases of instruments as well as in cases of their own. Some very elaborate compasses with screw and even rack and pinion drives to set the slider were known by 1850 and came in beautiful lizard-skin cases. Today they are much sought after by collectors.

In the nineteenth century one of the principal means of copying was by tracing. To assist with this awkward process, *tracers* were included in the catalogues of many of the well known instrument makers. They looked like ivory-handled pens but instead of nibs they had agate or steel points which could be run over the lines on the tracing paper. The plain agate-pointed instruments were generally considered to be the best, though the steel points were perhaps more attractive.

If original drawings were not too valu-

Proportional dividers were often supplied in expensive morocco or lizard-skin cases.

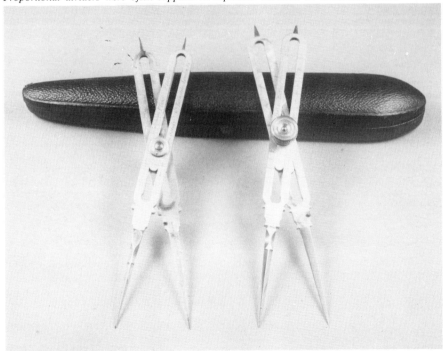

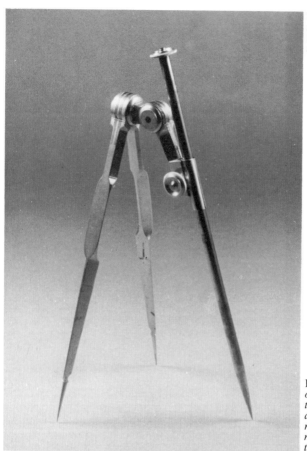

LEFT: *A 5 inch (127 mm) triangular compass or divider by Stanley, about 1897, showing its universal head joint.*

BELOW: *An ivory-handled opisometer. The screw-threaded bar is shown up against a stop. As the wheel is rotated along a line, the bar moves laterally through the centre of the wheel.*

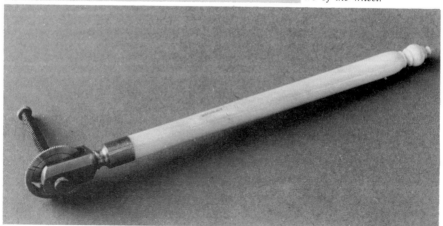

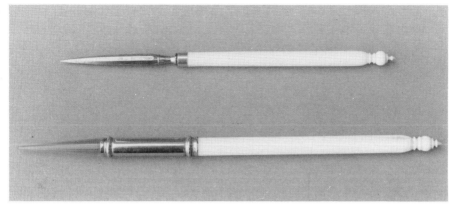

Two tracers. The upper one has a steel point, the lower an agate point, which was considered to be the better.

able, they could be copied by 'pricking out'. The drawing would be laid over another piece of paper and its principal points would be transferred to the surface beneath by pricking through with a very fine point. *Prickers* also looked like ivory-handled pens, and the nibs of some pens unscrewed to expose a sharp point at the base of the handle. Prickers were also much used in the accurate construction of angles, since a tiny hole could fix a point much more closely than a pen or pencil.

The *opisometer* was a useful device for measuring the length of an irregular line on a map or diagram. It consisted of a wheel held in bearings at the end of an ivory handle. Through the middle of the wheel was a screw-threaded rod, with stops at each end, which would move laterally as the wheel rotated. To measure the length of a line, the rod would be set up against a stop and the wheel run along the line. The device would then be picked up and run backwards along a scale until the rod returned to its original stop. Opisometers of this type are rare today.

A selection of prickers. The top one is a combined pen and pricker. Spare needles can be stored in the handles of the two lower ones.

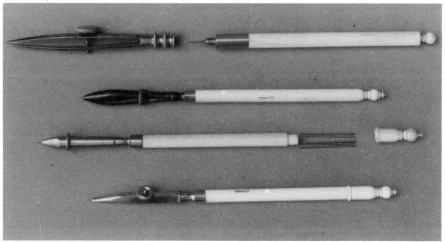

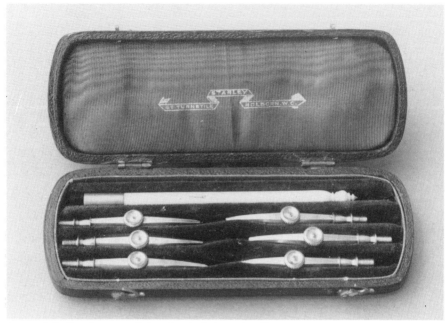

A set of six fine line pens fitting the single ivory handle.

PENS, RULES, SCALES AND CURVES

The most important element in any drawing is the line. Its quality — thickness, darkness, straightness and evenness — are of paramount interest to the draughtsman, as therefore are the instruments he uses for drawing it, normally the pens and the rule.

Most of the pens of the period looked very similar. They all consisted of two flat, pointed blades or nibs whose distance apart, and therefore the line thickness, was adjusted by a screw with a finely milled head. Most pens had ivory handles which were decoratively turned at the top. Indian ink was introduced between the blades by a small brush or dropper and was held there by capillary action in a column about 0.2 inch (5 mm) long. The pen was never dipped into the ink as this would cause the fluid to run out all over the blades. There were, however, variations in construction of the nibs and these differences in design influenced the intrinsic value of the pen.

The *fine line pen* was cut out of a single piece of steel, ensuring that each blade was equally firm when in contact with the drawing surface; the lines produced could be extremely fine. These pens were very difficult to clean as it was almost impossible to remove all traces of potentially corrosive ink from between the blades. When the blades wore down they became awkward to re-set, a task best left to the makers. Sets of six pens, fitting one ivory handle, were sold in small cases, and this eased the problems of cleaning and setting.

The *block pen* had two blades which were made separately and then soldered into a block of metal at the base to keep them apart. They held more ink but were usually cruder and cheaper than the fine line pen.

The *lifting nib pen* was made with the upper blade hinged at the base so that it could be raised to facilitate cleaning. A small spring between the blades kept them apart; adjustment of the screw caused the upper blade to move smoothly

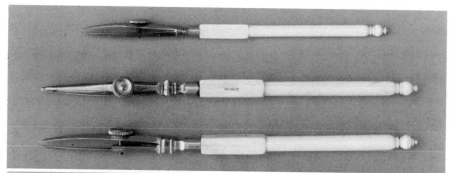

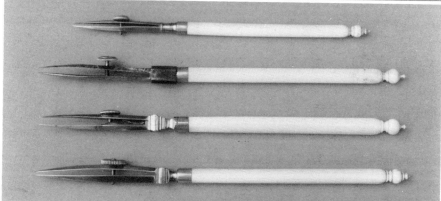

TOP: *Three pens with square sections on the handles designed to assist in gauging the correct angular position for holding the pen.*

ABOVE: *A selection of ivory-handled ruling pens: (from the top) fine; block; lifting nib with spring; specially hinged pen with no separate spring.*

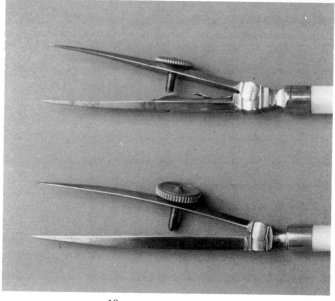

RIGHT: *The two versions of the lifting nib. The lower pen is of superior design with a very rigid lower blade and improved hinge with integral spring.*

19

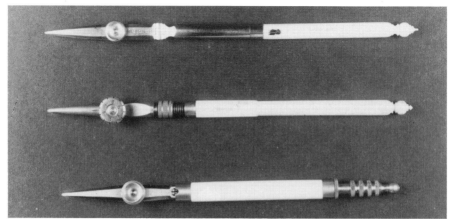

ABOVE: *Three unusual pens: (top) a handle of silver and ivory by Cary; (centre) a nib with line-thickness setting scale on the adjusting screw; (bottom) an unusual ivory and brass handle.*

BELOW: *Unscrewing the knurled brass top of the ivory handle frees the nib blades for cleaning. These unusual pens were always found in Army and Navy CS Limited, Woolwich sets.*

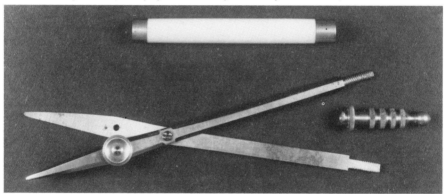

against the spring. These pens were very popular and widely used but suffered from a minor defect in that it was hardly possible to make the upper blade, with its joint, as rigid, laterally, as the lower one, which gave the lower nib a tendency to scratch. The ultimate variation found in the most expensive and highest class of pen embodied an upper blade constructed entirely of steel, which was continued back to form an integral, sprung part of the hinge. The lower nib was made very thick, except near the tip, which gave it the rigidity to prevent flexing when up against a rule, a fault in cheaper pens which led to variations in thickness of the line. No spring was placed between the blades.

All sorts of configurations of these basic two-bladed ruling pens were developed to meet different demands. The *road pen* was simply two sets of nibs side by side whose distance apart could be adjusted by a screw; it is an excellent device for ruling parallel lines. Similar to it was the *section pen* for drawing very close parallel lines. It had a third blade, not carrying ink, in order to locate a constant offset from the previously drawn line.

One of the most interesting devices, though difficult to use, was the *dotting pen*. It had small wheels, or rowels, with toothed edges, located between the

20

blades of the nib. Ink ran down on to the wheel, which rotated as it was moved across the drawing surface. The patterns of dots and dashes could be altered by changing the wheels. One manufacturer's pen could produce a line of dots 60 feet (20 m) long with one filling. It is very difficult to find these pens complete and in good condition nowadays.

Some prominent firms offered several hundred (one offered a thousand) different scales and undertook to manufacture others to meet the specific needs of customers. Only the more unusual items are discussed here.

Rules and scales were generally made of ivory or boxwood (Turkey wood). Ivory, which came from several parts of Africa and from Sri Lanka, tended to become discoloured and to shrink. Much of the best (green) ivory, taken from near the centre of the tusk, was sun-bleached and seasoned for up to eight years. Ivory became very expensive after about 1920 and this led to the much wider use of boxwood, which was itself sometimes seasoned for between seven and fifteen years. Unfortunately the legibility of the graduations on boxwood was liable to deteriorate, especially after long use. This led to the incorporation of opaque white celluloid for the edges of scales, very carefully applied so that the thickness of the boxwood counteracted the potential expansion and contraction of the celluloid.

The very accurate dividing engines developed by one of the leading makers were said to be capable of dividing down to at least a thousandth of an inch (0.02 mm), far more finely than it would be sensibly possible to mark, let alone read.

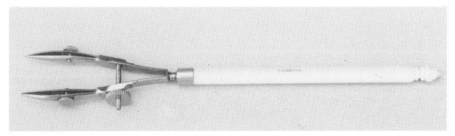

ABOVE: *A road pen for drawing parallel lines.*

BELOW: *A particularly fine dotting pen with patented ink feed to the wheels, made by Stanley about 1890. It has an ivory container for the spare dotting wheels at the top of the handle.*

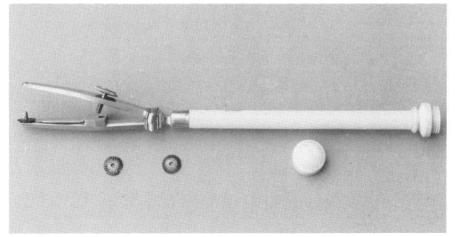

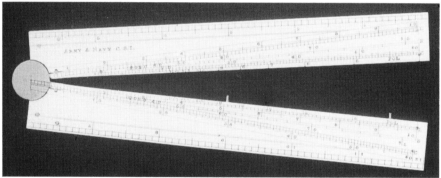

The reverse sides of two ivory protractors showing diagonal scales which were used in conjunction with dividers for very precise measurements. The lower rule also has a scale of chords (marked 'CHO') for constructing angles.

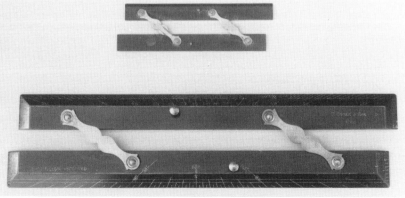

A 6 inch (152 mm) ivory sector showing some of its numerous trigonometrical scales. It dates from 1880.

Two ebony parallel rules of the bar type. The lower is 15 inches (381 mm) long and has angular markings for navigational purposes (Captain Field's pattern).

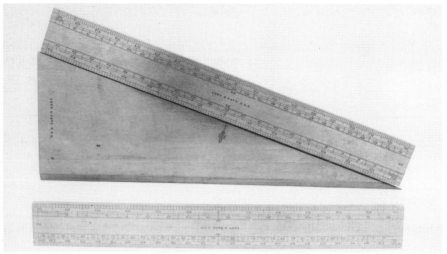

A set of Marquois scales in thick boxwood. These scales were used largely by the military, primarily for drawing accurately spaced lines.

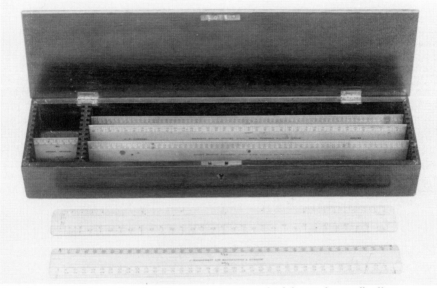

A mahogany case for scale rules. The compartment on the left was for small offsets.

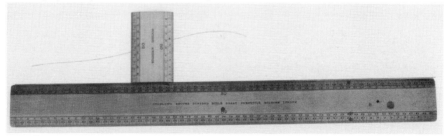

An offset being used in conjunction with a boxwood chain scale.

A selection of rolling parallel rules by Harling. The two in the centre, both brass, are superior because they have adjusting screws on the roller spindles.

The divisions themselves were about 0.002 inch (0.04 mm) thick. These machines were eventually driven individually by electric motors, which contributed to the great evenness of cutting.

One of the most intriguing and certainly the most versatile and ingenious of the rules found in the nineteenth century was the *sector,* which dates from about 1600. It was a veritable geometrical calculating device which, when used in conjunction with a compass, would contribute to the solution of many draughting problems. It was a jointed rule, generally having 6 inch (152 mm) arms. Upon it were ruled lines of sines, tangents, secants, logar-

ithms and chords as well as a scale of one foot divided into a hundred parts. A description of its use takes up twenty pages in the treatise by F. W. Simms while J. F. Heather devotes nine pages to it (see Further reading). The sector began to be replaced by comprehensive tables from about 1850, though it was still made for some years afterwards. By 1900 it was no more than an ornament in a set of instruments. Today it is much sought after by collectors.

Marquois scales were generally made of thick boxwood and consisted of two rules which were separately used in conjunction with a wooden triangle, two of

A selection of French curves. The three large pearwood curves date from 1880 and are still in perfect condition. The rest are of vulcanite.

24

whose sides were in the ratio of 3:1 by length. The triangle was moved against the rules to produce parallel lines of precise separation. Only the army had a use for these antiquated though very robust rules, which appeared in all the Sandhurst and Woolwich instrument sets until the end of the First World War.

The rules which are found most frequently today are 12 inch (305 mm) *chain scales,* engine-divided on boxwood as well as on ivory. There were six common scales used by civil engineers and surveyors, ranging from ten to sixty divisions to the inch. Small 2 inch (51 mm) rules called *offsets* were used in conjunction with the chain scales for plotting; their ends were made perfectly square so they could slide along the edge of the larger rule at right angles to it. These little rules are a mystery to many dealers and are often thrown away.

Parallel rules, both rolling and bar versions, were known by the beginning of the nineteenth century. The older bar type used to be made in ivory or ebony with brass, silver or electrum cross links.

Some had special angular scales engraved on them for navigational chart work. The much later rolling rules were made of ebony, boxwood, solid brass, gun metal or electrum; if the body was made of wood they sometimes had opaque white celluloid edges, divided in a variety of scales. The rules ranged in length from 6 inches to 36 inches (152mm to 914 mm) and were very heavy in the larger sizes. Modern rules of this type look much the same.

French curves, so readily available today in plastic, were made originally of pearwood, principally because its highly uniform density made it possible to produce a smooth edge in every direction to the grain. These curves have survived remarkably well. Vulcanite, a hard compound of rubber and sulphur, became very popular in the late nineteenth century, though it was expensive early on. Transparent celluloid appeared in 1870 and was widely adopted for the production of French curves. In about 1900 celluloid was around three times as expensive as pearwood.

PROTRACTORS AND SET SQUARES

Protractors are for setting up and measuring angles. Being so commonplace, they are taken for granted nowadays, but they first appeared more recently than might be expected because the mechanical operations involved in dividing the circle accurately into a number of equal parts were, until the second half of the eighteenth century, among the most difficult in engineering. The machines of the greatest significance developed for this purpose were the dividing engines of Ramsden (1768) and Troughton (1778), followed later by Cooke's circular dividing machines (1872), which held sway until 1909. These machines are displayed in the Science Museum in London.

Small rectangular protractors 6 or 4½ inches (152 or 114 mm) long and made of ivory or boxwood, occasionally of brass or electrum, were well known throughout the nineteenth century and were standard items in sets of instruments at least until 1950. The many subsidiary scales incorporated on these protractors were

generally too small to be of much use and the unequal spaces occupied by the angular graduations round the edges rendered these little rules useless for exact work. They were, however, favoured by army officers for sketching and laying off compass bearings on maps, a process assisted by the provision of vertical rulings on some special-purpose protractors to facilitate their alignment with the grid markings. These superficially attractive rules now command high prices which are out of proportion to their worth or usefulness.

Much more desirable are the plain circular protractors varying in diameter from 6 to 12 inches (152 to 304 mm). They were made mainly in brass or electrum, sometimes in vulcanite or celluloid, and were divided down to half a degree or better. Their extreme edges were bevelled thin and this made it possible for fine prickers to feel the angular engravings round the circumference. Semicircular protractors of the

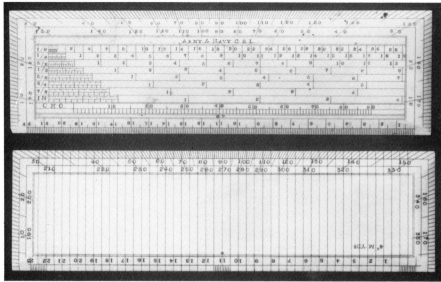

ABOVE: *Two 6 inch (152 mm) ivory protractors. The lower one was much favoured by the military for sketching since its vertical rulings allowed it to be easily aligned with reference or grid lines.*

BELOW LEFT: *A solid brass circular protractor, 6 inches (152 mm) in diameter, engraved to half a degree. The small semicircular protractor on the case is of silver.*

BELOW RIGHT: *A folding-arm protractor put away in its crude mahogany case.*

26

same type were also popular.

For higher accuracies, vernier scales were introduced and with their aid it became possible to measure down to a minute or so of arc. The best example of such a device was the *folding-arm protractor*. These superb instruments were graduated in much the same manner as a 6 inch (152 mm) theodolite, whose readings they were often used to plot. The folding arms had prickers at their extremities to mark off points very precisely. The arms moved on a frame about the centre of the protractor, where cross wires on glass served to locate the instrument at the point where the angle was to be set up. A clamp and tangent screw movement made it possible to adjust the setting of the arms with extreme precision so that the required angle could be pricked off very accurately.

The *isograph,* similar in appearance to a folding rule, had the head of its electrum or brass joint marked off in degrees so that the two arms of the rule could be set to any angle, albeit rather coarsely. The isograph was intended to be used primarily in conjunction with a tee-square for setting up corresponding left and right angles frequently occurring on a drawing. The largest isographs were 12 inches (304 mm) long when closed and

the best of these had attractive clamping screws on their head joints.

Set squares are still in wide use today. It was Stanley who introduced vulcanite, with its highly stable properties, for their general construction and many examples survive. The best large set squares were made of mahogany edged with ebony. They were very popular in hot climates, where they retained their shape accurately without warping because the grain ran longitudinally on all sides. The adjustable set square, so common today, became popular in the early part of the twentieth century. It was made of the newly developed celluloid; the finest ones had bevelled edges and electrum screws. This type of set square seems to have been a peculiarly British device.

A simple but very useful device was the *clinograph,* a set square with a swivelling arm. It was designed to be used in conjunction with a tee-square or straight edge, against which its base would rest. The arm could be set to any angle, which it would maintain by virtue of the friction joint. The clinograph could then be moved about the drawing to repeat the angle; if it was turned over, the angle could be reversed, which was most useful in the production of symmetrical figures.

TOP: *An electrum and boxwood 6 inch (152 mm) isograph. It would normally be used in conjunction with a tee-square.*

CENTRE: *A selection of set squares. The large 11½ inch (292 mm) examples are of mahogany with ebony edges. The small ones in the centre are of brass. The vulcanite set square (upper left) has a patented device to anchor it to the drawing surface.*

BOTTOM: *A good 10 inch (254 mm) mahogany clinograph by Thornton dating from about 1925. Here it is in use against a mahogany straight edge. Clinographs were useful for drawing repeated angles and, if desired, reversing them.*

RIGHT: *A fine set of small silver instruments supplied by Troughton and Simms, dating from 1866. The ivory protractor is only 4½ inches (114 mm) long.*

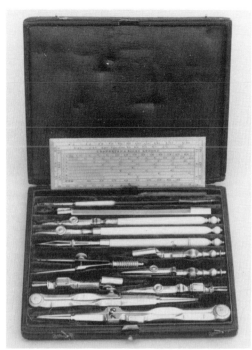

BELOW: *A fine 13 inch (330 mm) oak magazine case of instruments with two trays. It dates from 1916. Such sets as these used to be presented as prizes by some of the professional institutes.*

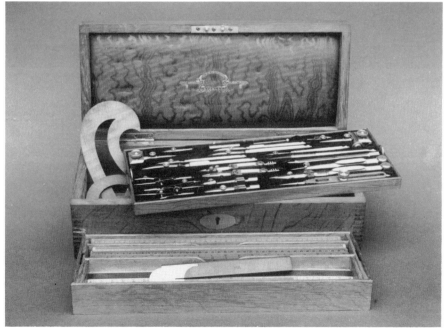

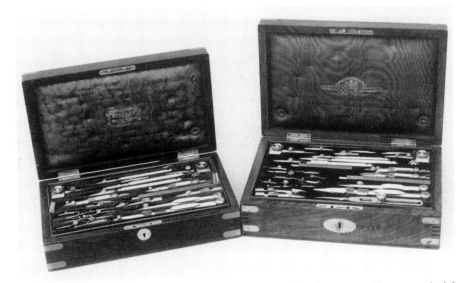

Two brass-bound mahogany and walnut magazine cases, each with two trays. The one on the left dates from 1890, that on the right from 1879.

COLLECTING

Collecting old drawing instruments can be an absorbing activity, especially if restoration becomes part of the hobby. It is instructive, too, for innovations in technology, the application of new materials and changes in drawing procedures are often reflected in the design of instruments.

Where the collector should look for interesting items depends on him and on how much he is willing to spend. Bric-à-brac stalls, junk shops, antique shops, local sales and charity outlets are all fruitful hunting grounds, while the major salerooms, specialist dealers and auctioneers sometimes handle highly valuable magazine cases of instruments. The buyer must beware of being overcharged, especially for sets. An unscrupulous dealer might fill the slots in an instrument tray with items which do not belong or even fit and then price it as a complete set. The best safeguard is to look for the maker's name, which should appear on the shanks of instruments made by good firms (with the exception of the smallest items and spring bow compasses).

Another test is to examine the knurling of the screw heads and the turning at the ends of the pen handles; these features were nearly always characteristic of the maker and they should be consistent throughout the set. Many owners had their names or initials engraved on every item in a case of instruments, including the rules in some instances; this information can help in detecting whether a set has survived intact. However, a beautiful set of instruments should not be rejected out of hand just because it is missing the odd pen or rule. It is more than likely that these items can be obtained elsewhere and the search increases the pleasure of collecting.

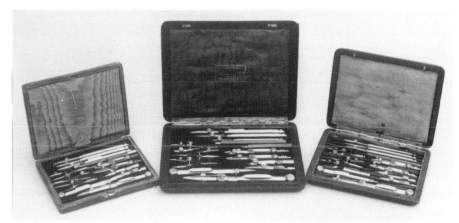

ABOVE: *Three top-grade 'pocket' cases of instruments. Being 6 to 8½ inches (152 to 216 mm) wide, they were too large to fit into any normal pocket.*

RIGHT: *A valuable presentation case of Stanley instruments, dating from 1880.*

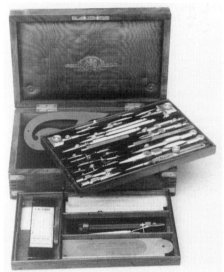

BELOW: *An array of instrument cases. They are mostly covered in Morocco leather; the large one in the centre is of Russian leather. Names or initials are engraved on the silver plates.*

FURTHER READING

Allen, C. J. *A Century of Scientific Instrument Making*. Harley Publishing Company, London, 1953. (A history of W. F. Stanley and Company Limited.)
Baynes, K., and Pugh, H. *The Art of the Engineer*. Lutterworth Press, 1981.
Booker, P. J. *A History of Engineering Drawing*. Northgate Publishing Company, London, 1979. (While it contains no specific details of instruments, it gives a fascinating insight into why types of instruments evolved.)
Hambly, Maya. *Drawing Instruments, Their History, Purpose and Use for Architectural Drawings*. British Architectural Library, London, 1982. (A beautifully illustrated catalogue and text for the RIBA Exhibition in 1982.)
Heather, J. F. *A Treatise on Mathematical Instruments*. Virtue Brothers and Company, London, seventh edition 1864.
Simms, F. W. *A Treatise on the Principal Mathematical Drawing Instruments*. John Weale, London, second edition 1845. (It devotes twenty pages to the sector.)
Stanley, W. F. *A Descriptive Treatise on Mathematical Drawing Instruments*. Privately published, 1866. (A fully descriptive and illustrated text of key importance. Available in major reference libraries.)
Stanley, W. F. (revised by Tallack). *Drawing and Mathematical Instruments*. E. and F. N. Spon, London, 1925.
Turner, Gerard L'E. *Antique Scientific Instruments*. Blandford Press, 1980.
Turner, Gerard L'E. *Nineteenth Century Scientific Instruments*. Sotheby, 1983.

PLACES TO VISIT

Museum of the History of Science, Old Ashmolean Building, Broad Street, Oxford OX1 3AZ. Telephone: Oxford (0865) 243997.
Royal Museum of Scotland, Chambers Street, Edinburgh EH1 1JF. Telephone: 031-225 7534.
Science Museum, Exhibition Road, South Kensington, London SW7 2DD. Telephone: 01-589 3456.
Whipple Museum of the History of Science, Free School Lane, Cambridge CB2 3RH. Telephone: Cambridge (0223) 358381 extension 340.

These fine brass-bound 10 inch (254 mm) cases display workmanship of the highest order.